Informal Assessments for
Reading Development

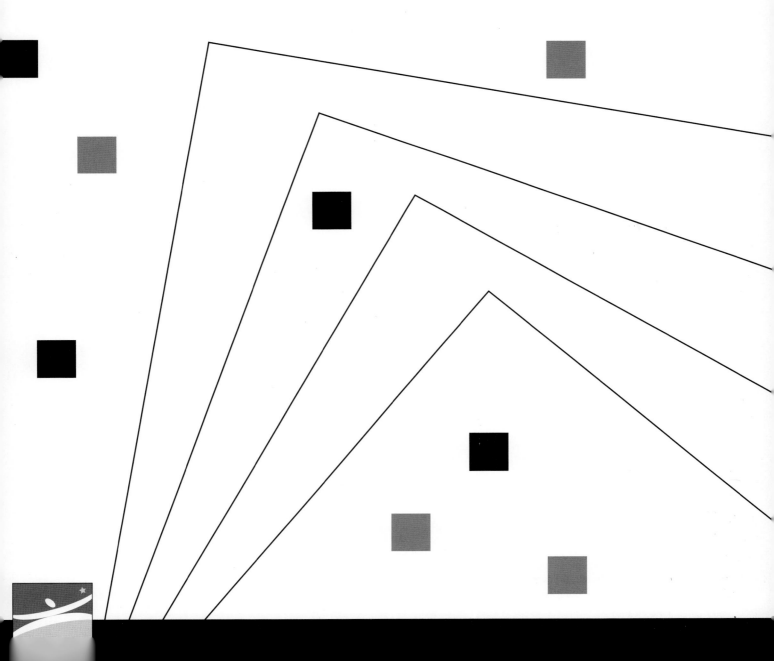

Benchmark Education Company
145 Huguenot Street • New Rochelle, NY 10801
www.benchmarkeducation.com

ISBN: 978-1-4509-0545-9

For ordering information, call Toll-Free 1-877-236-2465 or visit our Web site: www.benchmarkeducation.com.

Informal Assessments for Reading Development

Table of Contents

Benchmark EDUCATION
Building Literacy for Life™

Assessment Introduction

Daily teaching goes hand in hand with ongoing assessment and evaluation. The wide variety of reading, writing, spelling, and language assessments provided by Benchmark Education Company enables teachers to:

- obtain multiple perspectives on the literacy growth occurring in their classrooms;
- monitor and reflect on their teaching and students' learning;
- make informed decisions about students' progress and needs;
- select appropriate materials and instructional techniques that match students' current level of development;
- document progress over time through a cumulative portfolio;
- report progress to students, parents, and administrators.

Meaningful, ongoing, and multifaceted observation is the heart of the evaluation process. Since observations must occur in authentic contexts, utilize your small-group reading time to document students' efforts to join discussions; ask and answer questions; react to prompts; contribute ideas for graphic organizers; process texts; problem-solve new words; apply targeted skills and strategies, and act out and/or talk, draw, or write about books.

The integration of assessment, teaching, and learning supports effective literacy instruction. Benchmark Education Company provides teachers with the tools for understanding and documenting literacy development. Teachers can use this information to differentiate instruction by developmental reading behaviors and characteristics, metacognitive and comprehension strategy needs, instructional reading levels, fluency, and vocabulary understandings.

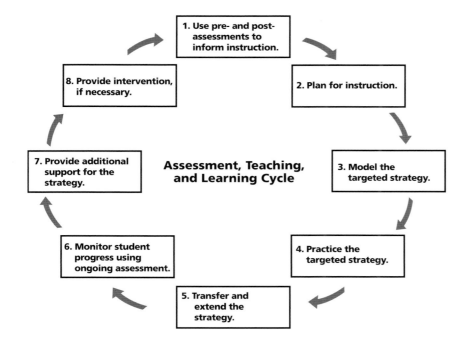

Assessment, Teaching, and Learning Cycle

1. Use pre- and post-assessments to inform instruction.
2. Plan for instruction.
3. Model the targeted strategy.
4. Practice the targeted strategy.
5. Transfer and extend the strategy.
6. Monitor student progress using ongoing assessment.
7. Provide additional support for the strategy.
8. Provide intervention, if necessary.

Rhodes and Shanklin (1993) outline the eleven principles of literacy assessment. Each of these principles is supported in every Benchmark Education Company assessment product.

11 Principles of Literacy Assessment	How BEC Assessment Tools Support the Principles
1. Assess authentic reading and writing.	A variety of ongoing informal assessment tools are available for use before, during, and after literacy instruction.
2. Assess reading and writing in a variety of contexts.	Assessment tools can be administered one-on-one, in small groups, or with the whole class.
3. Assess the literacy environment, instruction, and students.	Assessment tools prompt teacher reflection and provide direction on linking assessment results to instruction.
4. Assess processes as well as products.	Rubrics and assessment tools are available for lesson analysis and noting observable developmental behaviors and characteristics.
5. Analyze error patterns in reading and writing.	Oral reading records and rubrics identify error patterns, strengths, and needs.
6. Consider background knowledge in the assessment of reading and writing.	Student interest questionnaires and surveys gain insight into a students' literacy background and understandings.
7. Base assessment on normal developmental patterns and behavior in reading and writing.	A variety of reading behaviors and characteristics checklists are available to assist in noting developmental milestones and then reporting and planning during assessment meetings.
8. Clarify and use standards in the assessment of reading and writing.	Assessments are aligned with National Literacy Standards and state expectations for learning.
9. Use triangulation to corroborate data and make decisions.	Multiple assessments target different areas of literacy development and are designed to facilitate triangulation of data.
10. Involve students, parents, and other school personnel in the assessment process.	Sharing results from the Benchmark Education Assessments in data team meetings and parent conferences informs and involves others in the process of linking assessment and instruction.
11. Make assessment an ongoing part of everyday reading and writing opportunities and instruction.	Each assessment book provides guidance on how to schedule, manage, organize, and store assessments. Calendars and other planning tools are also provided.

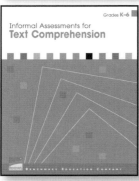

Benchmark Education Company Assessment

The Benchmark Education Company Assessment resources provide tools for ongoing literacy assessments. Each resource has a variety of planning and assessment tools that can be used to inform instruction. Assessment resources can be administered to the whole group, small group, or individual students.

Informal Assessments for Reading Development
- tools for documenting reading behaviors over time, acquisition of concepts about print, and English-language development
- oral reading records
- prompting guides
- reading conference note-taking forms that focus on characteristics of reading development

Informal Assessments for Text Comprehension
- tools for assessing metacognitive and comprehension strategy understandings
- tools for genre and text structure retellings
- comprehension prompting guides
- reading conference note-taking forms that focus on comprehension strategy development

Informal Assessments for Fluency Development
- tools for assessing accuracy, rate, prosody, and oral reading performances
- prompting guides
- reading conference note-taking forms that focus on fluency development

Informal Assessments for Vocabulary Development
- tools for assessing Tier One, Two, and Three vocabulary understandings
- prompting guides
- reading conference note-taking forms that focus on vocabulary development

Informal Assessments for Writing Development
- tools for assessing writing development
- rubric and checklists for assessing genre and text structure
- writing conference note-taking forms

Scheduling, Managing, Organizing, and Storing Assessments

Documenting progress through a cumulative portfolio is one of the greatest advantages of classroom-based assessment. Following are some tips to carry out this process in a teacher- and student-friendly manner.

Scheduling Assessments

Use some assessments as pre- and post-evaluations of growth and development, completing them at the beginning and end of the school year. Conduct other assessments on a more frequent basis as needed. Assess informally during literacy activities every day. Schedule an individual literacy conference with each student every month, and use the information in instructional planning. Hold additional reading and writing conferences as needed to meet students' immediate needs, allowing students to schedule conferences with you as well. Assess students in greatest need of intervention or additional instructional support more frequently—every one to two weeks.

Planning Calendars

Planning calendars help teachers schedule and manage assessments throughout the school year. Teachers can use the masters in the Appendix to note key dates for administering and gathering assessment data for an entire class or individual students.

Year-at-a-Glance Planning Calendar Record state, district, and classroom scheduled assessment dates. (See Appendix page 66)

Month-at-a-Glance Planning Calendar Record progress-monitoring assessments for the entire class or 1–3 students per day. (See Appendix page 67)

Week-at-a-Glance Planning Calendar Record progress-monitoring assessments and individual reading conferences for the week. (See Appendix page 68)

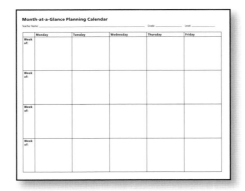

Managing Assessments

Start with one assessment tool and gradually build to the desired collection, as indicated in the following implementation steps.

1. Organize your classroom learning environment. Establish consistent routines and clear expectations for a variety of instructional settings, including whole-group, small-group, and independent activities.

2. Create a management system and schedule for administering formal and informal assessment measures. Identify a simple storage and retrieval system. Set a manageable schedule.

3. Start slowly and proceed one student at a time until all are assessed and you have identified their literacy developmental stages, strengths, and needs.

4. Create class profiles of your findings to serve as a lesson-planning reference and cumulative documentation of growth. Update the profile with each month's individual student conference data.

5. Reflect on the information gathered:

   Are students progressing in a timely fashion?

   What is their overall growth during a specified time frame?

   Are your goals for students being met?

   Is your assessment informing instruction and vice versa?

   Do you see transfer of the skills, strategies, and behaviors you have modeled and taught?

   Do the students in your class reflect the national standards and expectations for their grade level?

Organizing and Storing Assessment Materials

A simple plan for collecting and retrieving each type of record will ensure success and ongoing implementation.

Color code and use separate pocket folders or three-ring binders for each aspect of literacy to be assessed. Have a clearly identified and labeled location to house the individual student assessment folders or binders. Within each folder or binder, use dividers and pockets to store the completed individual assessment tools and work samples.

Store the completed group profile charts in lesson-planning books or create a separate three-ring binder. The binder can serve as an instructional reference tool and cumulative documentation of teaching and learning. Use index tab dividers to note the different profile charts to be collected and used over a school year. Include national, state, and district grade-level recommendations and expectations to complete this instructional reference binder.

Observations and Responsive Teaching

Daily observations of students engaged in meaningful literacy experiences provide detailed information regarding literacy development, strengths, and needs. Documenting observations on a regular basis provides opportunities for teachers to reflect on instruction and areas in need of further assessment. Tomlinson & McTighe remind us that "Responsive teaching suggests a teacher will make modifications in how students get access to important ideas and skills, in ways that students make sense of and demonstrate essential ideas and skills, and in the learning environment—all with an eye to supporting maximum success for each learner." Observations of student learning and transfer provide the link between the assessment and instruction process.

Anecdotal Notes

Anecdotal notes are the observations that are written by the teacher during or after a literacy event. These detailed notes capture students' processing behaviors so they may be further analyzed and used to inform the next instructional move. Anecdotal notes can be taken in whole- or small-group settings or for individuals. These informal notes contain valuable information about students' strengths, weaknesses, progress, needs, processing abilities, or any other observations teachers feel are significant.

Use the Anecdotal Notes master (Appendix page 69) to record notes and observations. Place one small sticky note in each box (one per student). After recording the student's name, date, and your observations, transfer the sticky notes to individual students' portfolios.

What Research Says About Reading Development

"Sometimes assessment is administered and the results recorded, but then the process stops. Teachers are unsure what to do with the data or where to go next in their teaching."

—Fountas & Pinnell

Reading development assessment tools help teachers pinpoint where students are on the continuum of literacy development and in turn, where instruction needs to go next and strengths to build upon. *Informal Assessments for Reading Development* help teachers to use their observations to be responsive and identify needs, form flexible groups, prompt for support, and notice characteristics of readers over time.

Marie Clay reminds us that *"to improve teaching, teachers need to observe children's responses as they learn to read and write and watch for:*

- *Competencies and confusions*
- *Strengths and weaknesses*
- *Evidence of processing and strategic activities*
- *Evidence of what the child can already control."*

Research About Reading Development Assessment and Instruction	How *Informal Assessments for Reading Development* Supports Best Practices
"…what I hope for teachers is that they notice the details of children's development and theorize about why particular children do what they do." (Johnston)	Observant and responsive teaching is supported through the use of Individual Reading Conferences and guidance to help teachers notice the characteristics of reading development over time.
"…it is helpful to keep in mind the general expectations of readers at a level so that books may be well selected and appropriate support may be given to individuals and groups." (Fountas & Pinnell)	Reading Developmental Checklists and Oral Reading Records provide evidence of growth and control of the reading process and aid teachers in text selection for small-group and independent reading.
"Having taken the record, teachers can review what happened immediately, leading to a teaching decision on the spot, or at a later time as they plan for next lessons. They can judge what the reader already knows, what the reader attended to, and what the reader overlooked. They can assess how well each reader is pulling together what he or she already knows about letters, sounds, and words in order to get to the messages. This kind of information allows teachers to prompt, support, and challenge individual learners. The records allow teachers to describe how children are working on a text." (Clay)	Oral reading records and tools for analyzing and scoring are provided to help teachers support each stage of reading development.
"Assessing metacognition allows us to discover students' perceptions of themselves as readers and writers, the reading and writing they do, and the strategies they employ to solve the problems they encounter in reading and writing." (Rhodes & Shanklin)	Self-assessments encourage students to reflect on their understandings of being proficient readers, their attitudes, habits, and use of strategies to monitor and maintain comprehension.
"Feedback from a teacher becomes part of the information students use for internal regulation and learning. Feedback creates opportunities for students to grow by giving them insights about their work that they might not be able to come up with on their own." (Moss & Brookhart)	Prompting stems provide teachers with the language to support reading development and support student needs and strengths.

Developmental Checklists

Readers generally move through four developmental stages as they learn to read. The stages are emergent, early, transitional, and fluent. Understanding the developmental stages and their characteristics enables teachers to select appropriate materials and methodologies to support all learners. A variety of assessment tools can be used to note reading development and progress over time for individual students and small groups of learners. Additional checklists that focus on first language reading behaviors and experiences and English-language development are provided to support the language and literacy acquisition of English learners. Use these assessment tools periodically throughout the year to record observations and notations of student growth.

Observation Checklist of First-Language Reading Behaviors and Experiences

Name _____ Date _____

Directions: Students who are new to the English language may utilize emergent texts in small-group instruction. However, based on their prior first-language literacy behaviors and experiences, they may progress at different rates. Use this checklist to help you identify the level of support each of your new ELs may need.

Literacy Behaviors and Experiences	Yes	No	Do Not Know
Student has attended school on a regular basis.			
Student can show how a book is read.			
Student recognizes familiar illustrations and photographs from literature.			
Student can read in his or her first language.			
Student can write in his or her first language.			
Student can find first-language cognates in English texts.			

Based on your observations, use the following suggestions to inform your instructional decisions.

If the student does not exhibit age-appropriate reading behaviors in his or her first language, you will need to provide intensive support and instruction in both English language and literacy. This student may need extended instruction using emergent *Early Explorers* reading materials.

If the student demonstrates age-appropriate reading behaviors in his or her first language, the student is likely to make rapid literacy progress directly correlated with English-language development.

Notes: _____

_____

_____

English-Language Development Observation Checklist

Directions: Use your observations to informally assess student's level of English-language development based on TESOL levels. Combine the results with the Observation Checklist of First-Language Reading Behaviors and Experiences (page 13) to help you place students into appropriate text levels. Then focus instruction on the characteristics marked "Never" or "Sometimes" to enable the student to progress in his or her language acquisition.

TESOL Level 1	Never	Sometimes	Consistently
Communicates nonverbally			
Understands little spoken English			
Observes during instruction			
Relies heavily on pictures for comprehension			
Displays limited English reading comprehension			
TESOL Level 2			
Uses basic words, phrases, and expressions			
Memorizes simple phrases and sentences			
Relies on some nonverbal communication			
Begins to follow instructions and class discussions			
Begins to comprehend in reading with support			
TESOL Level 3			
Occasionally joins in conversations and class discussions on familiar topics			
Produces longer phrases and complete sentences with some grammatical errors			
Displays increasing comprehension			
Relies on high-frequency words and known patterns			
TESOL Level 4			
Sometimes uses academic language			
Engages in conversations and class discussions			
Uses more complex sentences and phrases with fewer grammatical errors			
Begins to use multiple strategies to communicate and comprehend			
Composes original writing			
TESOL Level 5			
Frequently uses academic language			
Produces language comparable to a native speaker (with a few grammatical errors)			
Actively participates in all areas of literacy—speaking, listening, reading, and writing			
Uses multiple strategies to communicate and comprehend			

Concepts About Print Assessment

Name _____ Date _____

What to Ask	What to look For	Results	
Where is the cover?	Student points to the cover.	☐Yes	☐No
Where is the title?	Student points to the title on the cover.	☐Yes	☐No
Where is the author's name?	Student points to the author's name on the cover.	☐Yes	☐No
How should I open the book?	Student correctly demonstrates how to open the book.	☐Yes	☐No
Where is the first page?	Student points to the title page.	☐Yes	☐No
Where is the top of the page?	Student points to the title at the top of the page.	☐Yes	☐No
Where is the bottom of the page?	Student points to the author's name at the bottom of the page.	☐Yes	☐No
(Turn to a spread.) Where are some words?	Student points to any words on the page.	☐Yes	☐No
Where is a picture?	Student points to the photo or drawing on the page.	☐Yes	☐No
Where should I start reading?	Student points to the first word on the page.	☐Yes	☐No
How should my finger move as I read?	Student moves finger left to right under the line of print.	☐Yes	☐No
Can you point to the words as I read this line?	Student correctly demonstrates one-to-one matching as you read.	☐Yes	☐No
How many words are in this line?	Student correctly identifies the number of words in the line.	☐Yes	☐No
Where should I start reading next?	Student points to the first word on the second line of print.	☐Yes	☐No
Where is an uppercase letter on the page?	Student points to an uppercase letter at the beginning of any sentence.	☐Yes	☐No
Can you point to the first letter in a word?	Student points to the first letter in any word.	☐Yes	☐No
Can you point to the last letter in a word?	Student points to the last letter in any word.	☐Yes	☐No
(Point to a period on any page.) What is this punctuation mark? What does it mean?	Student says "It tells you stop because the sentence is done" or gives a similar explanation. Student says "period."	☐Yes	☐No
(Point to a question mark on any page.) What is this punctuation mark? What does it mean?	Student says "Someone is asking something" or gives a similar explanation. Student says "question mark."	☐Yes	☐No
(Point to an exclamation point on any page.) What is this punctuation mark? What does it mean?	Student says "It means you use an excited voice" or gives a similar explanation. Student says "exclamation point."	☐Yes	☐No
(Point to a comma on any page.) What is this punctuation mark? What does it mean?`	Student says "It tells you to pause" or gives a similar explanation. Student says "comma."	☐Yes	☐No

Individual Reading Observation Checklists

Using a Reading Observation Checklist of observable behaviors allows teachers to focus attention on what a student understands about the reading process. The assessment measures student understanding in the areas of linking prior knowledge, reading for meaning, developing vocabulary, developing comprehension, and responding to the text.

Administration

1. Once a month, or on a regular basis, schedule time to observe each student reading independently.

2. Copy the Individual Reading Observation Checklist form for each student's stage of development or grade level.

3. On each form, record the student's name and the date.

4. Prior to the observation, read through the checklist to become familiar with the list of behaviors you may be observing while the student is reading.

5. For each criterion, determine if the student is at the beginning, progressing, or proficient stage of reading development.

6. Check the appropriate column for behaviors that are at the beginning, progressing, and proficient stages.

7. Ask the student to read aloud from the text.

8. Record any observations or comments made during the oral reading at the bottom of the page. If needed, conduct a brief interview for additional information regarding a student's understanding of particular reading behaviors.

9. After analyzing, place the Individual Reading Observation Checklist in the appropriate organized storage location.

Using the Results

1. After completing the checklist, review the form to determine the behaviors the student demonstrates control over in his or her reading development.

2. Determine which one or two next most important teaching points are needed for the student's development. Consider the areas checked off in the beginning column. Choose the teaching points based upon the student's strengths and areas of greatest need.

3. Plan to conduct a reading conference or lesson to address the areas of greatest need in an individualized setting.

Individual Guided Reading Observation Record · Levels A/1–C/4

Name _____ Date _____ Text Title_____ Text Level_____

Reading Behavior	Beginning	Progressing	Proficient
Reads fluently; problem-solves on one or two things only			
One-to-one matching			
Directionality			
Return sweep			
Knows a small core of high-frequency words that can be read fluently			
Self-monitors and attends to print, using high-frequency words			
Aware of errors and searches the picture as well as the print			
Rereads by returning to the beginning of the sentence			
Cross-checks prediction at point of difficulty with the picture and print			
Rereads at point of difficulty and articulates the first letter of the problem word			

Comments/Concerns:

Individual Reading Observation Record · Levels D/5–E/8

Name _____ Date _____ Text Title_____ Text Level_____

Reading Behavior	Beginning	Progressing	Proficient
Reads fluently; problem-solves on one or two things only			
Returns to reread closer to the point of difficulty			
Beginning to search through a difficult word for additional information by blending letters into sounds			
Fluently uses beginning chunks, or parts of words, and ending sounds			
Meaning and structure are guiding the reading			
Integrating meaning, structure, and visual cues; is moving towards automaticity			
Self-monitoring, or checking on him or herself; moving toward automaticity			
Analyzes words using graphophonic patterns			
Reads high-frequency words fluently			
Recognizes errors when reading and initiates problem-solving actions			

Comments/Concerns:

Individual Reading Observation Record · Levels F/9–I/16

Name _____ Date _____ Text Title_____ Text Level_____

Reading Behavior	Beginning	Progressing	Proficient
Reads fluently; problem-solves on one or two things only			
Problem-solves at the point of error and makes multiple attempts to self-correct			
Searches through the difficult word and blends sounds together			
Takes words apart using large units or syllables			
Meaning and structure guide the reading; uses visual information to check on reading			
Reads longer texts with greater accuracy			
Uses word meaning and context clues to problem-solve			
Increasing control of visual patterns and flexible use of strategies			
Reads high-frequency words fluently			

Comments/Concerns:

Individual Reading Observation Record · Levels J/18–M/28

Name _____ Date _____ Text Title_____ Text Level_____

Reading Behavior	Beginning	Progressing	Proficient
Uses nonfiction text features to locate information on a topic, including table of contents, headings, glossaries, boldfaced print, indices			
Interprets and uses nonfiction text features such as maps, charts, tables, flow charts, diagrams, time lines			
Decodes text using knowledge of common letter-sound correspondences, including blends, digraphs, consonant variants, r-controlled vowels, and a variety of spelling patterns			
Decodes text using knowledge of the structure of words such as endings, prefixes, suffixes, compound words, contractions, and root words			
Identifies variant sounds of consonants and vowels			
Integrates meaning, structure, and visual cues to decode and comprehend text			
Uses strategies of sampling, predicting, confirming, and self-correction independently			
Makes inferences from texts			
Reads longer, less-predictable texts with complex text structures			
Identifies nonfiction text structures such as descriptive, problem/solution, time/order, compare/contrast, cause/effect, and directions			

Comments/Concerns:

Individual Reading Observation Checklist · Levels N/30–X/60

Name _____ Date _____ Text Title_____ Text Level_____

Competency	Beginning	Progressing	Proficient
Linking Prior Knowledge			
• Relates prior experiences to the topic of the book			
• Makes connections from one text to another			
• Makes connections from the text to the outside world			
Reading for Meaning			
• Identifies purpose for reading			
• Identifies text features that will be useful			
• Determines the text structure organization			
• Asks questions to self when reading			
• Clarifies confusing parts by rereading, defining unfamiliar words, using graphic features, and skimming			
Developing Vocabulary			
• Uses knowledge of word structures (such as root words, inflectional endings, compound words, contractions, prefixes, suffixes) to determine word meaning			
• Uses context clues to determine word meaning			
• Identifies synonyms, antonyms, homonyms			
• Understands denotation and connotation			

Individual Reading Observation Checklist · Levels N/30–X/60

Name _____ Date _____ Text Title_____ Text Level_____

Developing Comprehension	Beginning	Progressing	Proficient
• Uses text features (such as table of contents, headings, captions, sidebars, glossary, index, bold print) to locate information			
• Uses graphic features (such as maps, charts, tables, time lines, graphs, diagrams) to interpret information			
• Summarizes or paraphrases information			
• Makes predictions			
• Makes inferences			
• Compares and contrasts information			
• Draws conclusions			
• Identifies main idea and supporting details			
• Identifies sequence or steps in a process			
• Identifies cause and effect			
• Analyzes text structure and organization (such as descriptive, comparative, sequential/time order, cause/effect, problem/solution, procedural, narrative)			
• Analyzes character			
• Analyzes story elements (setting, plot, theme, genre, mood, narrative point of view)			
• Interprets figurative language			
• Evaluates author's purpose and point of view			
• Evaluates fact and opinion			
• Makes judgments			
• Creates graphic organizers to retell, compare and contrast, or summarize the information			
• Identifies themes of the text			
• Applies knowledge learned from text in various situations			
• Evaluates texts for accuracy			
• Draws conclusions from the texts			

Informal Assessments for Reading Development ©2011 Benchmark Education Company, LLC

Small-Group Reading Observation Records

Small-group lessons allow teachers to focus instruction on the strengths and needs of selected students. Observations made during small-group instruction aid in the selection of group members and potential teaching points. Observations also allow the teacher to note student growth and development. This assessment measures the reading behaviors observed during a small-group reading lesson. Teachers can use this assessment periodically to note behaviors observed in an instructional setting.

Administration

1. Make a copy of the Small-Group Reading Observation Record.

2. Fill in the group members' names, the date, text title, and level.

3. After conducting a small-group reading lesson, fill in your observations of students' reading behaviors, teacher prompting, and the validation or activation of teaching points.

Using the Results

1. Review the notes recorded on the completed Small-Group Reading Observation Records.

2. Determine the one or two most important reading behaviors or strategies students in this group need as the focus for instruction. Identify any trends or patterns for teaching points to be addressed at the whole-group level.

3. Consider the membership of your small-group reading groups. Is it time to move students to other groups for maximum instructional effectiveness?

4. Place the Small-Group Reading Observation Records in the appropriate organized storage location. Keeping cumulative records provides a useful reference for future instruction.

Small-Group Reading Observation Record

Group members _____   Date _____

Text _____   Level _____

Check one:
   Before Reading _____   During Reading _____   After Reading _____

Teacher Prompt: **Students' Behavior:**

Comments:

Focus for next small-group reading lesson:

Small-Group Guided Reading Observation Checklists

The Small-Group Guided Reading Observation Checklist serves as a quick reference check for classroom teachers. When complete, it provides an overview of the group's reading abilities and points to areas that may need to be addressed in future lessons.

Administration

1. Once a month, collect and analyze the Individual Reading Observation Checklists you have completed for each student in your class.

2. Make one copy of the Small-Group Guided Reading Observation Checklist sheet.

3. Record the date of the checklist analysis at the top of the Small-Group Guided Reading Observation Checklist sheet.

4. After analyzing each individual checklist, transfer the information you learned about each student to the Small-Group Guided Reading Observation Checklist sheet.

5. Record the stage of development for each student and each criterion. Place an asterisk for behaviors that are at the proficient stage, a check mark for progressing, and an "X" for beginning.

Using the Results

1. After completing your Small-Group Guided Reading Observation Checklist chart, begin your analysis for growth and development, lesson planning, and intervention lessons.

2. Look for trends, patterns, and information that stand out.

3. Identify the areas you marked with a check mark or "X." These are the behaviors you will want to use as the focus for whole-group, small-group, or individual lessons.

4. Consider the number of students exhibiting the same stage of development for a particular behavior. If the majority of students are at the progressing stage, you may want to focus a small-group lesson for those students at the beginning stage.

5. If you notice a behavior that is at the beginning stage of development for most of your class, this can become the focus of your whole-group lessons. Remember to first model the behavior for your students, allow them the opportunity to participate with you in a shared-reading lesson, and then reinforce the behavior in a small-group reading lesson, or an individual lesson if needed.

6. The behaviors that stand out as individual concerns may be addressed in small-group or individualized lessons.

7. After analyzing, place Individual Reading Checklists and your Small-Group Guided Reading Observation Checklist in the appropriate organized storage location.

Small-Group Guided Reading Observation Record · Levels A/1–C/4

Date: _____

Text Title: _____

Text Level: _____

Chart Coding Legend:
✓ reading behavior observed during lesson

Student's Name:

	Reads fluently; problem-solves on one or two things only	One-to-one matching	Directionality	Return sweep	Knows a small core of high-frequency words that can be read fluently	Self-monitors and attends to print, using high-frequency words	Aware of errors and searches the picture as well as the print	Rereads by returning to the beginning of the sentence	Cross-checks prediction at point of difficulty with the picture and print	Rereads at point of difficulty and articulates the first letter of the problem word

Comments/Concerns: _____

_____

_____

_____

_____

_____

_____

_____

Small-Group Guided Reading Observation Record · Levels D/5–E/8

Date: _____

Text Title: _____

Text Level: _____

Chart Coding Legend:
✓ reading behavior observed during lesson

Student's Name:	Reads fluently; problem-solves on one or two things only	Returns to reread closer to the point of difficulty	Beginning to search through a difficult word for additional information by blending letters into sounds	Fluently uses beginning chunks, or parts of words, and ending sounds	Meaning and structure are guiding the reading	Integrating meaning, structure, and visual cues; is moving towards automaticity	Self-monitoring, or checking on him or herself; moving toward automaticity	Analyzes words using graphophonic patterns	Reads high-frequency words fluently	Recognizes errors when reading and initiates problem-solving actions

Comments/Concerns: _____

_____

_____

_____

_____

_____

_____

_____

Small-Group Guided Reading Observation Record · Levels F/9–I/16

Date: _____

Text Title: _____

Text Level: _____

Chart Coding Legend:
✓ reading behavior observed during lesson

Student's Name:

	Reads fluently; problem-solves on one or two things only	Problem-solves at the point of error and makes multiple attempts to self-correct	Searches through the difficult word and blends sounds together	Takes words apart using large units or syllables	Meaning and structure guide the reading; uses visual information to check on reading	Reads longer texts with greater accuracy	Uses word meaning and context clues to problem-solve	Increasing control of visual patterns and flexible use of strategies	Reads high-frequency words fluently

Comments/Concerns:

_____

_____

_____

_____

_____

_____

_____

Small-Group Guided Reading Observation Record · Levels J/18–M/28

Date: _____

Reading Behaviors	Student Names								COMMENTS/ CONCERNS
• Uses nonfiction text features to locate information on a topic, including table of contents, headings, glossaries, boldfaced print, indices									
• Interprets and uses nonfiction text features such as maps, charts, tables, flow charts, diagrams, time lines									
• Decodes text using knowledge of common letter-sound correspondences, including blends, digraphs, consonant variants, r-controlled vowels, and a variety of spelling patterns									
• Decodes text using knowledge of the structure of words such as endings, prefixes, suffixes, compound words, contractions, and root words									
• Identifies variant sounds of consonants and vowels									
• Integrates meaning, structure, and visual cues to decode and comprehend text									
• Uses strategies of sampling, predicting, confirming, and self-correction independently									
• Makes inferences from texts									
• Reads longer, less-predictable texts with complex text structures									
• Identifies nonfiction text structures such as descriptive, problem/solution, time/order, compare/contrast, cause/effect, and directions									

Small-Group Guided Reading Observation Checklist
Levels N/30–X/60

Date _____   Grade _____

Student Names									
Linking Prior Knowledge									
• Relates prior experiences to the topic of the book									
• Makes connections from one text to another									
• Makes connections from the text to the outside world									
Reading for Meaning									
• Identifies purpose for reading									
• Identifies text features that will be useful									
• Determines the text structure organization									
• Asks questions to self when reading									
• Clarifies confusing parts by rereading, defining unfamiliar words, using graphic features, and skimming									
Developing Vocabulary									
• Uses knowledge of word structures (such as root words, inflectional endings, compound words, contractions, prefixes, suffixes) to determine word meaning									
• Uses context clues to determine word meaning									
• Identifies synonyms, antonyms, homonyms									
• Understands denotation and connotation									

Small-Group Guided Reading Observation Checklist
Levels N/30–X/60

Date _____   Grade _____

Student Names										
Developing Comprehension										
• Uses text features (such as table of contents, headings, captions, sidebars, glossary, index, bold print) to locate information										
• Uses graphic features (such as maps, charts, tables, time lines, graphs, diagrams) to interpret information										
• Summarizes or paraphrases information										
• Makes predictions										
• Makes inferences										
• Compares and contrasts information										
• Draws conclusions										
• Identifies main idea and supporting details										
• Identifies sequence or steps in a process										
• Identifies cause and effect										
• Analyzes text structure and organization (such as descriptive, comparative, sequential/time order, cause/effect, problem/solution, procedural, narrative)										
• Analyzes character										
• Analyzes story elements (setting, plot, theme, genre, mood, narrative point of view)										
• Interprets figurative language										
• Evaluates author's purpose and point of view										
• Evaluates fact and opinion										
• Makes judgments										
Responding to the Text										
• Creates graphic organizers to retell, compare and contrast, or summarize the information										
• Identifies themes of the text										
• Applies knowledge learned from text in various situations										
• Evaluates texts for accuracy										
• Draws conclusions from the texts										

Reading Conferences

Individual Reading Conferences provide teachers with an opportunity to hear students read aloud orally from a self-selected title, or familiar reading of a text from small-group guided reading lessons. When observing students as they read aloud orally, conduct an oral reading record and record anecdotal notes regarding how fluently students are reading. The Reading Conference recording form provides a template for key elements to include in your reading conferences.

Use the fluency rubric found on page 60 to note accuracy, rate, and expression. After listening to students read aloud orally, you may choose to provide additional support through mini-lessons, prompts (see also pages 34 to 43), or discussions related to linking fluent reading and overall comprehension of the text.

Individual Reading Conference

Student Name: _____ Date: _____

Book Title: _____ Author: _____ Pages _____ to _____

Part One: Independent Reading Recap

Why did you choose this book? What are you interested in reading about? Do you need help finding a new book?

How is the difficulty of the text for you? How do you know?

Summarize or retell what has been happening (or what you have learned) so far.

Tell me what you remember most about what you've read.

Notes: _____

_____

Part Two: Reading Development Connections

How have you used the fix-up and monitoring strategies we've been learning about as a reader?

How have they helped you understand what you are reading? Explain.

How do you know when you have a breakdown in understanding what you are reading? How do you adjust your reading? How does that help you understand, or comprehend the text more?

Notes: _____

_____

Part Three: Oral Reading Record

Conduct an oral reading record on the independent reading selection or from a text read previously in Small-Group Guided Reading lessons.

Attach the oral reading record form to your Individual Reading Conference note-taking form when finished.

Record notes for observations and next steps instructionally below.

Notes: _____

_____

Part Four: Action Planning

What are your strengths/needs/goals as a reader? How can I help you achieve them?

When do you anticipate finishing this book?

What is next on your list of must-read titles?

Notes: _____

_____

Prompting to Support Reading Development

As an observant and responsive teacher, having a variety of prompting stems for a variety of purposes is a valuable resource. Each type of prompt has a distinct purpose for supporting learning and increasing proficiency with the elements of fluency. The following pages contain prompting stems to support readers for a variety of reasons. Use the prompts during guided practice or during independent reading. Remember to continually ask students to reflect on what they understand and how they fix up and monitor their reading to support comprehension. This will promote awareness of the link between decoding, fluency, vocabulary, and comprehension, and aid in encouraging students to reflect and monitor reading to maintain understanding at all times.

Responsive Teaching Prompts

Prompting Type	Purpose	Prompts
Goal Oriented	Prompts for the reader who is not using the targeted strategy or skill at all. They offer a model or a benchmark of how the strategy or skill is used in reading.	Listen to how I… Read it like this ____. Watch how I … ____is not ____. When I ____ I ____. Notice what I do when I ____. Describe/define ____. Point out example ____. I'm going to ____. Listen to how I read this.
Corrective Feedback/ Directive	Prompts for students who are beginning to use the strategy or skill but still need direct teaching or coaching on how to use it properly.	Now read ____. Can you ____? Do this ____. Change this ____. Try that again and _____. Try doing this ____. Repeat after me ____. Read it like this ____. Put ____. Take ____. Make ____. Read ____.
Self Monitoring/ Reflective	Prompts for students who have previously exhibited use of the strategy or skill in reading but are not consistent. These prompts remind students to be more reflective and think about the importance of using the strategy or skill at the right time.	How did you ____? How did you know ____? What did you notice about ____? Did you have any trouble ____? Was your reading ____or ____? I noticed ____. When did you know to ____? What made you ____? Where did you ____?
Validating/ Confirming	Prompts that are used at any time to validate or confirm a student's reading strategies and skills.	I like the way you ____. Good job at ____. You ____. I noticed ____. You took ____. You made ____. You are ____.

Prompts to Support the Integration of Cueing Systems

A critical force in developing a strategic reader is to use specific language to direct the student's attention on how to integrate multiple sources of information. Through the following language prompts, readers learn how to check one source of information against another in order to gain important feedback from the text (Clay, 1993b).

Does the word make sense?

Does the word sound right?

Does the word look right?

Does the word make sense and look right?

Does the word look right and sound right?

____ makes sense, but look at the first letter.

During literacy events, teachers use language to communicate specific knowledge, skills, and strategies to students. Language prompts make students aware of problem-solving processes and provide immediate feedback that explicitly describes an acceptable literacy behavior. For learning to occur, the student must understand the intent of the teacher's language so that he may successfully perform the prompted task. The following language prompts help students focus on appropriate strategies for problem-solving in reading and writing (Clay, 1991; Dorn, et al., 1998; Fountas and Pinnell, 1996).

Do you think that word could be _____?

Are you right?

Go back and read that again.

Is there anything else you can do?

What did you notice?

Read it again and see if you can find out what is wrong here.

Is there something you can do to help yourself?

What is the book about?

Do you know something about that word that can help you?

How would you begin that word if you were writing it?

What sound do you hear in the word _____? Say it slowly.

Do you see a word on this page that has those letters?

Assisted-reading events, such as shared reading and guided reading, help students develop strategies for gathering meaning from many experiences with a variety of texts. These guided-participation settings allow the teacher and the students to engage in interactive conversations about how printed language works. Through focused discussions, demonstrations, and language prompts, students acquire higher levels of processing behavior in order to operate more effectively on text. Analysis of oral reading records and writing samples provide teachers with excellent opportunities to observe the students' processing behavior and to respond accordingly.

Prompts to Support Metacognitive and Comprehension Strategies

Ask Questions

Good readers wonder about the text to help them understand it.

Ways to Ask Questions

- Ask questions about unfamiliar words or confusing information
- Ask questions that have answers right in the text
- Ask questions that have answers that can be inferred from the text
- Ask questions that are not answered in the text and will need further research

PROMPTS to Help Readers Ask Questions

- What does the word _____ mean on this page?
- I wonder what the author means when he says …
- I wonder if [a character] is going to …
- Why is the author giving me so much information about _____?
- What would I do if I were in the same situation as [a character]?
- I wonder what else I could learn about . . .

Determine Text Importance

Good readers identify and evaluate important information in the text.

Ways to Determine Text Importance

- Activate and build prior knowledge.
- Determine what is important versus what is interesting.
- Distinguish between what to read carefully and what to ignore.
- Highlight important words and nonfiction text features (captions, labels, bullets, etc.).
- Make notes and drawings in the margin to understand and remember the text.
- Determine author's perspective, point of view, and/or opinion.

PROMPTS to Help Readers Determine Text Importance

- I know these parts of the story are important because . . .
- I think these parts of the text are interesting because …
- I think the author thought _____ is important because . . .
- I need to pay attention to this _____. It has information I need.

Fix-Up Monitoring

Good readers monitor and fix-up their comprehension when it breaks down.

Ways to Monitor and Fix-Up
- Reread to clarify
- Stop and think about what you read
- Stop and write about what you read
- Ask questions
- Read ahead
- Talk about what you read

PROMPTS to Help Readers Monitor and Fix-Up
- I didn't understand that. Maybe I should reread it more slowly.
- Wait a minute. I need to stop and think.
- Wait a minute. I need to stop and write about that.
- The author says _____. What does that mean?
- I'm not sure what's happening. I think I'll read ahead and see if it becomes clearer.
- Who could I talk to about this to understand it better.

Make Connections

Good readers link what they read to something they already know.

Ways to Make Connections

Text-to-Self: The reader makes a personal connection with the text.

Text-to-Text: The reader makes a connection between the text she is reading and a text she has already read.

Text-to-World: The reader makes a connection between the text and something in the world at large.

PROMPTS to Help Readers Make Connections
Text-to-Self:
- This reminds me of when I . . .
- I knew someone just like this when I . . .
- I had the same experience when . . .

Text-to-Text:
- This character is just like the character in . . .
- The plot of this story is so similar to the plot of . . .
- I remember reading another book that took place in the same setting . . .

Text-to-World:
- If this character were alive today, I bet she would be _____.
- What's going on in this book is just like what's happening right now in . . .

Make Inferences

Good readers use clues in the text to figure out something the author has not stated.

Ways to Make Inferences

- Using story clues to figure out what is happening or why it is happening
- Using clues about characters (their actions, words, thoughts) to figure out what they are like and what they might do next
- Using clues to figure out the book's themes, or "big ideas"

PROMPTS to Help Readers Make Inferences

- The author says _____. I think she means . . .
- If I read between the lines, the author is telling me . . .
- The clues that prove my inference are . . .
- I think the character did this because . . .
- I think this happened because . . .
- These few pieces of evidence tell me that . . .
- From the information in this chapter (section), I can infer that . . .
- From the events in the story so far, I think _____ will happen next.
- The picture (photograph) on the cover of the book suggests that . . .
- The graphics on page _____ suggest that . . .
- I know more about _____ because of the specific information I read on page _____.

Summarize & Synthesize

Good readers form new ideas or perspectives.

Ways to Summarize & Synthesize

- Summarize information by stating the big ideas.
- Make generalizations, judgments, and opinions.
- Distinguish between more important ideas and less important ideas.
- Stop to collect their thoughts about a topic before, during, and after reading.

PROMPTS to Help Readers Summarize & Synthesize

- This story or passage is really about . . .
- So far I know _____. This makes me think that . . .
- My opinion of _____ is _____. I think this because the text said . . .
- This helps me understand . . .
- My thinking about this topic has changed because . . .

Visualize

Good readers form pictures in their minds to "see" what the author has written.

Ways to Visualize

- Vivid verbs that describe actions

- Adjectives that describe size, shape, color, and other details

- Graphic features (charts, maps, time lines, diagrams, etc.) that tell size, shape, length, distance, time, and other information

- Similes and metaphors that compare one thing to another

- Sensory language that evokes how something feels, sounds, smells, or tastes

PROMPTS to Help Readers Visualize

- In my mind, I see ...

- The words _____ help me really see [the character or setting] in my mind.

- The author's description makes me imagine a place that is . . .

- I've never seen a _____, but I imagine it is . . .

- I can [smell/taste/feel/hear]...

Analyze Character

Good readers use clues and evidence in the text to make inferences about characters.

PROMPTS to Help Readers Analyze Character

- What clues tell you that [character] is _____?

- You can tell that [character] is …

- I know [character] is _____ because …

Analyze Story Elements

Good readers examine the literary elements in a story—its characters, setting, and plot—to develop an appreciation and understanding of the work.

PROMPTS to Help Readers Analyze Story Elements

- What clues tell you where the story takes place?

- The problem in the story is …

- What clues tell you about [character]?

Compare and Contrast

Good readers find ways that two things are alike and/or different.

PROMPTS to Help Readers Compare and Contrast

- How are _____ and _____ alike? How are they different?

- What do _____ and _____ have in common?

- What words in the text can help you know when the author in comparing two [things/people/places]?

Distinguish & Evaluate Fact & Opinion

Good readers distinguish between facts and opinions and use this information to make inferences, draw conclusions, and make judgments.

PROMPTS to Help Readers Distinguish and Evaluate Fact and Opinion

- You can tell _____ is an opinion because …

- How do you know _____ is a fact?

Draw Conclusions

Good readers use information in the text and their background knowledge to determine what the author is suggesting without directly stating it.

PROMPTS to Help Readers Draw Conclusions

- From the information in this passage, you can conclude that …

- In what way is _____ important in the text?

Evaluate Author's Purpose

Good readers determine why the author wrote the passage or why specific information or text and graphic features are included.

PROMPTS to Help Readers Evaluate Author's Purpose

- The author probably included paragraph _____ so that _____.

- The author probably included the [text/graphic feature] so that _____.

- The author probably wrote this text to _____.

Identify Cause & Effect

Good readers find things that happened (effects) and why they happened (causes).

PROMPTS to Help Readers Identify Cause And Effect

- Why did _____ need to _____?

- What caused _____ to happen?

- What effect did _____ have on _____?

Identify Main Idea & Supporting Details

Good readers use information in the text to determine what a paragraph, passage, or chapter is mostly about.

PROMPTS to Help Readers Identify Main Ideas And Details

- What details in Chapter _____ support the main idea that …?

- What sentence in paragraph _____ best states the main idea?

Identify Sequence of Events

Good readers can determine the order of events for topics such as history, science, or biography.

PROMPTS to Help Readers Identify Sequence Of Events

- After [event or time], what happened?
- When can you _____?
- What happened first?
- What happened after _____?

Make Inferences

Good readers use clues and evidence in the text to determine what the author is suggesting without directly stating it.

PROMPTS to Help Readers Make Inferences

- What can you infer from _____?
- Which sentence from the text shows you that _____.
- What clues help you figure out what is happening?

Make Judgments

Good readers use facts from the text and their existing beliefs to evaluate an author's positions or to formulate opinions about characters and events in a text.

PROMPTS to Help Readers Make Judgments

- Do you agree with the author that …? Why?
- What should [character] have done when _____? Why do you think this?
- If you had written this text, what would you have said?

Make Predictions

Good readers use clues and evidence in the text to determine what might happen next.

PROMPTS to Help Readers Make Predictions

- What will [character] probably do in the future?
- What clues/evidence would support the prediction that …?

Summarize Information

Good readers use clues and evidence in the text to make inferences about the characters.

PROMPTS to Help Readers Talk About Character

- What clues tell you that [character] is _____?
- You can tell that [character] is …
- I know [character] is _____ because …

Assessment Walls

"The assessment wall makes the data visible, thus serving two important purposes: to study learning trends in student groups and to study reading progression for all students in relation to proficiency standards."

—Dorn and Soffos, 2001

Assessment walls (or folders) are used for identifying developmental progress (and strengths) as well as pinpointing instructional needs. Data can be displayed on a dedicated wall for faculty or grade level data meetings, or in file folders for classroom use. Assessment walls can be used flexibly to examine student growth as a class, small group, or individual learners.

When reviewing data at data team meetings or individually, consider the following questions as you reflect on student learning and next steps for instructional decisions.

How has the student(s) progressed? What are their strengths? Needs?

What instructional methods or interventions are supporting learning, or not?

What are your goals for instruction, next steps for planning and supporting learning?

Data team meetings and the use of assessment walls that focus on fluency development provide opportunities to identify observable behaviors that link decoding, word recognition, vocabulary and comprehension. Milestones included in the reference chart below as well as scores from using the Oral Reading Record Forms on page 55 provide discussion topics to consider when reviewing assessment data and reflecting on student learning and progress.

Reading Development Over Time

Developmental Reading Stages	Observable Reading Behaviors
Emergent (A/1– E/8) At the Emergent Stage, readers are learning what reading is all about. They are learning that a book has a special way of telling a story. They are learning that when you read a book, you start on the left page and move to the right. They are beginning to understand one-to-one matching when reading. Emergent readers are also learning how to read print using first letter cues and locating known high-frequency words. An important instructional focus is knowing how to support beginning readers as they learn to integrate meaning, structural, and visual cues.	Uses one-to-one matching. Uses proper directionality, or left to right. Follows return sweep. Knows a small core of high- frequency words that can be read fluently. Rereads at point of difficulty and articulate the first letter of the problem word. Self-monitors or check reading, using high-frequency words. Rereads independently to confirm or revise predictions. Rereads by returning to the beginning of the sentence. Checks prediction at point of difficulty using the picture (cross-checking).
Early (F/9– I/16) Early readers are becoming skilled at using visual and phonological information. They are displaying knowledge of reading high-frequency words with ease. They are learning to search beyond the first letter in a word at points of difficulty. They are beginning to initiate various problem-solving actions on unknown words such as rereading and cross-checking other cue sources. The goal of the Early Stage is for the reader to integrate their use of the cueing system (meaning, structure, and visual) automatically.	Rereads closer at the point of difficulty. Begins to search through a difficult word for more information. Fluently uses beginning chunks (parts of words) and ending sounds. Searches through the difficult word and blends sounds together. Integrates meaning, structure, and visual cues; moves toward automaticity.
Early/Fluent (J/18–M/28) At the transitional stage, readers have full control over early reading strategies and are developing strategies that enhance comprehension and thinking on a higher level. They use multiple sources to gain and infer meaning, including graphic sources, fonts and special effects, and text features (table of contents, glossary, index, etc.). Transitional readers have a wider vocabulary and use refined decoding skills on a regular basis. Due to these abilities, they read longer, complex texts with a greater degree of understanding. Readers at this stage shift from reading texts orally to primarily reading text silently.	Problem-solves at the point of error and makes multiple attempts to self-correct. Takes words apart using large units or syllables. Reads longer text with greater accuracy. Uses word meanings and context clues to problem-solve. Demonstrates increasing control of visual patterns and flexible use of strategies.
Fluent (N/30–X/60) Fluent readers are comfortable using all sources of information to gain and infer meaning. They read longer, complex texts from multiple genres (fiction, nonfiction, poetry) for longer periods of time. Decoding and vocabulary strategies are used automatically, and the text is read with orchestrated phrasing and fluency. Fluent readers continue to develop higher-level thinking and comprehension strategies. They are at a stage where important tools for learning can be acquired through reading.	Uses parts of a book, such as table of contents, headings, and glossaries to locate information. Accurately interprets graphic features of text, such as diagrams, tables, and charts. Monitors comprehension and uses appropriate fix-up strategies, such as asking questions, making predictions, and rereading. Connects what is read with personal experiences, other texts, and world events (to obtain the author's message and predict outcomes). Decodes a wide array of visual patterns and word parts. Uses context clues, such as definitions, descriptions, and examples to obtain the author's message.

Oral Reading Records

Oral Reading Records are detailed assessments that include teacher observation, recording of reading behaviors, and analysis of miscues. Oral Reading Records are administered individually in order to evaluate reading behaviors, guide instruction, check the difficulty of text, and monitor and document progress.

An Oral Reading Record allows the teacher to record observations, compare them with the text, and reflect on the strategies the students are using. The Oral Reading Record Analysis form provides a format for recording such information as scoring results, cues used and neglected, processing behaviors and strategies, and comprehension.

Instructions for Administering, Scoring, and Analyzing Oral Reading Records

Administration

1. Make a copy of the Oral Reading Record Analysis Form (see pages 56 to 59) and the Oral Reading Record form (see page 55) for each student.

2. Conduct an Oral Reading Record using a seen or unseen text. Use the Benchmark Education Recommended Titles for Oral Reading Records found on pages 51 to 54 to assist your selection of texts at various text levels.

Oral Reading Records allow you to observe a student without offering assistance. Only if the student has exhausted all problem-solving abilities should you give a prompt. As the student reads, use the following coding system for recording errors and miscues.

After recording the oral reading and listening to the student retell the text, analyze the observations. A close look at the student's **scoring, cues used and neglected, processing behaviors and strategies, and comprehension/ retelling check** helps you make an informed decision about the student's progress and future learning needs. Let's discuss these categories one by one.

Reading Behavior	Definition	Code
Accurate Reading	Reading without error	Place a ✓ over the word.
Substitution	Substituting an incorrect word for the correct word in the text	Draw a line over the word and write the student's word above the line: make / made
Omission	Leaving out a word or phrase	Draw a line over the word(s) and a dotted line above it: --------- / made
Insertion	Adding a word or phrase not included in the text	Draw a line at the point of error. Write the word(s) above the line and a dotted line below it: he / ----
Repetition	Repeating a word or phrase	Draw an arrow (➜) from the point of error to show how far back the student reread, whether it was a word, phrase, paragraph, or page.
Self-Correction	Correcting an error without assistance	Draw a line over the word. Write the error above the line, then add SC: make SC / made
Use of Visual Cues	Using letter and sound cues to problem-solve a word	Draw a line over the word and indicate the student's vocalizations above: m-a-d / made

Scoring

To determine the **error rate**, divide the number of words by the number of errors and round the result to the nearest whole number (X). This creates a ratio of 1:X. Next, locate the ratio on the chart below. Always go DOWN to the next lower number if the exact ratio is not shown. (For example, if your ratio is 1:16, go to 1:14 on the chart.) Finally, locate the corresponding **percent of accuracy**.

Error rate	1:100	1:50	1:35	1:25	1:20			
Accuracy Percentage	99	98	97	96	95			
Proficiency	Independent							

Error rate	1:17	1:14	1:12.5	1:11.75	1:10			
Accuracy Percentage	94	93	92	91	90			
Proficiency	Instructional							

Error rate	1:9	1:8	1:7	1:6	1:5	1:4	1:3	1:2
Accuracy Percentage	89	87.5	85.5	83	80	75	66	50
Proficiency	Frustrational							

To determine the self-correction (SC) rate, add together the errors and the SCs and then divide by the number of SCs to create a ratio of 1:X. In general, SC rates of 1:1–1:2 (excellent) or 1:3–1:5 (good) indicate that a student is monitoring appropriately and discovering information in the text that signals when something is wrong.

Cues Used or Neglected

Cues are simply defined as sources of information within the text. A reader constantly builds and integrates the networks of information and uses them to check and confirm responses. After the student reads, analyze each error and self-correction according to the meaning, structure, or visual cue used.

Semantic (Meaning) cues relate to the author's intended message and purpose as well as the reader's background knowledge and identification of particular concepts found within the text. Graphic features such as pictures, diagrams, and maps also help the reader gain access to the text's meaning.

Syntactic (Structural) cues are derived from the reader's oral language and exposure to book talk which allows him or her to predict upcoming text. Good readers monitor grammatical substitutions by asking, "Does it sound right this way?"

Graphophonic (Visual) cues relate to the letters, sounds, and words incorporated into a text. These elements require the reader to access the visual information in order to problem-solve.

The Oral Reading Record Analysis Form provides space on which to analyze and note cue sources used or neglected. For each error and self-correction, determine which cue source likely prompted the response by asking yourself questions such as:

Did the student use meaning to self-correct errors?

Are the student's errors meaningful? Does the reading still make sense even though the wrong word was used?

Are the student's errors grammatically correct?

Did the student use visual information in making attempts, errors, or self-corrections?

Processing Behaviors and Strategies

Next, analyze the behaviors and strategies the student uses both while reading fluently and at points of difficulty. Strategies are defined as problem-solving actions the reader employs to gain meaning from the text, such as:

- predicting future events
- anticipating language structures and patterns from text
- rereading to self-monitor
- cross-checking one cue source with another
- searching for visual patterns and elements
- self-correcting when aware of dissonance
- reading fluently and expressively
- problem-solving flexibly according to different purposes
- building on background knowledge to make sense of the text
- searching graphic features such as pictures, diagrams, maps, and tables for meaning
- using text features such as the table of contents, headings, glossary, and index to read for a purpose

The following questions can guide you in this stage of analysis:

Does the student reread to confirm meaning?

Does the student search for meaning in the pictures, diagrams, and tables?

Does the student search for visual patterns?

Does the student cross-check cue sources?

How does the student attempt unknown words?

Does the student appeal for help at points of difficulty?

Does the student wait to be told a problem word?

Are multiple cues used in self-correction?

Are various strategies used when problem-solving?

Was the text read fluently and with expression?

Comprehension/Retelling Check

To assess comprehension, ask the student to tell about the book in his or her own words. Record the response on the second page of the Oral Reading Record, and follow up with the comprehension questions. Finally, determine the student's level of understanding by analyzing his or her knowledge of the text's main idea and the number and type of details included in the retelling and answers.

Using the Results

1. Review the information gathered. Consider how this information will affect your instruction.

   • Are the needs of this student similar to those of others in the class?

   • Would some students benefit best from small group or individual lessons?

   • What is the impact of your findings regarding text level difficulty?

   • Is this level a good choice for the student at this time?

   • Would some students benefit from having a more difficult or easier text?

   • Is a student showing signs of monitoring his/her reading and utilizing fix-up strategies?

   • Is the student comprehending and reading for meaning?

   • Did the student respond to the text reflectively?

2. Staple the Oral Reading Record Analysis Form on top of the Oral Reading Record form and place in the appropriate, organized storage location.

Benchmark Education Recommended Titles for Oral Reading Records

TITLE	LEVEL	GENRE
My Backpack	A/1	Fiction
Balloon Ride	A/1	Fiction
Fun at the Beach	A/1	Fiction
What Do Communities Have?	A/1	Nonfiction
Life at the Beach	A/1	Nonfiction
Toy Models	A/1	Nonfiction
I Like	B/2	Fiction
Hat Day at the Zoo	B/2	Fiction
We Fish	B/2	Fiction
Animal Homes	B/2	Nonfiction
Homes for People	B/2	Nonfiction
Our Pets	B/2	Nonfiction
Costume Party	C/3	Fiction
A Party for Rabbit	C/3	Fiction
On a Coral Reef	C/3	Nonfiction
A Map of My House	C/3	Nonfiction
Soft and Hard	C/3	Nonfiction
Sam	C/4	Fiction
Tim the Tortoise	C/4	Fiction
The Birthday Flowers	C/4	Fiction
Farm Work	C/4	Fiction
A Pair of Babies	C/4	Nonfiction
A Plant Has Parts	C/4	Nonfiction
Our Families Help	C/4	Nonfiction
Farm Alarm	D/5	Fiction
Little Cat Goes Fast	D/5	Fiction
The Cake	D/5	Fiction
What Is in a Forest?	D/5	Nonfiction
In the Forest	D/5	Nonfiction
What Is Slow? What Is Fast?	D/5	Nonfiction
The Yard Sale	D/6	Fiction
At the Park	D/6	Fiction
Every Tree Has a Life Cycle	D/6	Nonfiction
Rainy Day, Sunny Day	D/6	Nonfiction
Going to Town With Mom and Dad	D/6	Nonfiction
Remember the Rules!	E/7	Fiction
Sit, Sam	E/7	Fiction
The Hungry Fox	E/7	Fiction
Ponds	E/7	Nonfiction
Three Kinds of Water	E/7	Nonfiction

TITLE	LEVEL	GENRE
Rules at School	E/7	Nonfiction
Not Now, Sam	E/8	Fiction
Little Chick	E/8	Fiction
Garden Lunch	E/8	Fiction
Helping Animals	E/8	Nonfiction
A Seed Needs Help	E/8	Nonfiction
The Four Seasons	E/8	Nonfiction
Animal Families	E/8	Nonfiction
Little Lion	F/9	Fiction
The Ants Have a Picnic	F/9	Fiction
Jake's Sleepover	F/9	Fiction
Rocket Ship Shapes	F/9	Fiction
Ocean Animals	F/9	Nonfiction
Watch a Frog Grow	F/9	Nonfiction
Food in the Forest	F/9	Nonfiction
Wendy the Water Drop	F/10	Fiction
How Raven Became Black and Owl Got Its Spots	F/10	Fiction
Counting Clues	F/10	Fiction
Big Ben Helps the Town	F/10	Fiction
Summer to Fall	F/10	Nonfiction
Counting Insects	F/10	Nonfiction
The Arctic	F/10	Nonfiction
A New Friend	G/11	Fiction
Sam Is Special	G/11	Fiction
Sam Finds the Way	G/11	Fiction
How Does A Cactus Grow?	G/11	Nonfiction
Looking at Matter	G/11	Nonfiction
People Work in Our Community	G/11	Nonfiction
Paul Bunyan	G/12	Fiction
A Good Pick	G/12	Fiction
A Trip to the Market	G/12	Fiction
The Race to Recycle	G/12	Fiction
All About Trees	G/12	Nonfiction
What Is Motion?	G/12	Nonfiction
What Is a Good Citizen?	G/12	Nonfiction
Everyone Clapped For Jason	H/13	Fiction
Caterpillar Can't Wait	H/13	Fiction
Bitsy the Beaver	H/13	Fiction
A Rainbow Party	H/13	Fiction
Watch a Butterfly Grow	H/13	Nonfiction
Food in the Ocean	H/13	Nonfiction
Insects All Around	H/13	Nonfiction
The Farm Stand Mystery	H/14	Fiction
See You in Spring	H/14	Fiction

TITLE	LEVEL	GENRE
The Very Mean King	H/14	Fiction
Maggie Makes Macaroni	H/14	Fiction
Trees	H/14	Nonfiction
The States of Matter	H/14	Nonfiction
Winter to Spring	H/14	Nonfiction
Charlie's Championships	I/15	Fiction
Shrimp Joins the Team	I/15	Fiction
The Lost Pirate	I/15	Fiction
Finding Fossils	I/15	Nonfiction
Animals' Eyes and Ears	I/15	Nonfiction
Do Plants Grow Under Water?	I/15	Nonfiction
A Throne for the King	I/16	Fiction
A Happy Summer Day	I/16	Fiction
The Great Green Forest	I/16	Fiction
Miss Keen Needs Help	I/16	Fiction
What Are the Parts of a Tree?	I/16	Nonfiction
A Volunteer Helps	I/16	Nonfiction
In a Tropical Rain Forest	I/16	Nonfiction
The Mystery of the Missing Cookie	J/18	Fiction
The Royal Zookeeper	J/18	Fiction
How Animals Change and Grow	J/18	Fiction
Plants and Animals in Different Seasons	J/18	Nonfiction
My Neighborhood	J/18	Nonfiction
Ants	J/18	Nonfiction
The Bee Puzzle	K/20	Fiction
The Earth on Turtle's Back	K/20	Fiction
Stump Hill	K/20	Fiction
The Great, Big, Giant Turnip	K/20	Fiction
Honeybees Help Flowers	K/20	Nonfiction
Making Rules	K/20	Nonfiction
In the Backyard	K/20	Nonfiction
The King's Mapmaker	L/24	Fiction
The Big Party	L/24	Fiction
Mondo and Gordo Weather the Storm	L/24	Fiction
How We Group Animals	L/24	Nonfiction
Good Citizens	L/24	Nonfiction
Frances the Fairy Dressmaker	L/24	Fiction
Earth's Water Cycle	L/24	Nonfiction
All About Continents	L/24	Nonfiction
The Cooking Contest	M/28	Fiction
Environmentally Friendly World	M/28	Fiction
Samantha Saves the Stream	M/28	Fiction
Pete Discovers Gravity	M/28	Fiction

TITLE	LEVEL	GENRE
It's Earth Day	M/28	Nonfiction
Polar Habitats	M/28	Nonfiction
The Amazon	M/28	Nonfiction
Opening Night	N/30	Fiction
Why Polar Bears Like Snow . . . and Flamingos Don't	N/30	Nonfiction
Three Ancient Communities	N/30	Nonfiction
The Three Little Pigs Wise Up and the Princess, the Prince, and the Vegetables	N/30	Fiction
Storm Chasers	N/34	Fiction
From Caves to Canvas	O/34	Nonfiction
The Life Cycle of Plants	O/34	Nonfiction
Max's Glasses	P/38	Fiction
Liquids and Gases	P/38	Nonfiction
Habitats of Australia	P/38	Nonfiction
The Treehouse Club	Q/40	Fiction
Colonial Times	Q/40	Nonfiction
What Makes an Animal an Animal?	Q/40	Nonfiction
After the Earthquake	R/40	Nonfiction
The Magic Passport	R/40	Fiction
Doomed to Disappear? Endangered Species	R/40	Nonfiction
The Ogs Discover Fire and Other Stuff	S/44	Fiction
Martians are People, Too	S/44	Fiction
Tsunamis	S/44	Nonfiction
Weather Works	S/44	Nonfiction
Voices from the Civil War	T/44	Nonfiction
Plant Genetics	T/44	Nonfiction
Escape to Freedom: The Underground Railroad	U/50	Nonfiction
Trackers of Dynamic Earth	U/50	Nonfiction
The Seven Wonders of the Ancient World	V/60	Nonfiction
The Life of a Star	V/60	Nonfiction
Women in the Renaissance	W/60	Nonfiction
Ecological Disasters	W/60	Nonfiction
Volcanoes: Nature's Awesome Power	X/60	Nonfiction
Energy Resources Around the World	X/60	Nonfiction

Oral Reading Record

Student's Name _____ **Date** _____

Text Title _____ **Level** _____

Reading Level _____ **Score** _____

Page #	Text	Cues used: Errors			Cues used: Self-Corrections		
		M	S	V	M	S	V
Totals:							

Comments:

Key to Cues
M = meaning
S = structure
V = visual

Oral Reading Record Analysis: Levels A/1–E/8

Directions: Use the prompts below to further analyze students' oral reading records.

Name _____ Date _____

School _____ Teacher _____

Text Title _____

Text Level _____ Seen _____ Unseen _____

Scoring			
Scores:	1: ___ Error Rate	___% Accuracy	1: ___SC Rate	
The scores are at the:	___Independent Level	___Instructional Level	___Frustrational Level	
Cues Used and Neglected			
On errors, the student predominantly uses:	___meaning cues	___structure cues	___visual cues	
On self-corrections, the student predominantly uses:	___meaning cues	___structure cues	___visual cues	
Processing Behaviors and Strategies			
The student appears to control:	___one-to-one matching on one-syllable words	___one-to-one matching on multisyllable words	___directionality left to right	
	___directionality on return sweep	___locating known words	___locating unknown words	
At a point of difficulty, the student:	___shows flexible use of strategies	___self-corrects using different cues	___cross-checks cue sources	
	___appeals for help	___rereads to confirm	___uses pictures	
	___uses the first letter	___searches for visual patterns	___uses known words to solve unknown words	
	___waits to be told	___attempts unfamiliar words	___makes multiple attempts	
The student:	___reads word-by-word	___uses fluent phrasing	___uses expression	___uses punctuation
Comprehension/Retelling Check			
When retelling, the student's knowledge of the text's main idea:	___is lacking	___is teacher prompted	___is accurate	
When retelling, the student uses:	___no details	___few details	___several details	___extensive details

Oral Reading Record Analysis: Levels F/9–I/16

Directions: Use the prompts below to further analyze students' oral reading records.

Name _____ Date _____

School _____ Teacher _____

Text Title _____

Text Level _____ Seen _____ Unseen _____

Scoring			
Scores:	1: ___ Error Rate	___% Accuracy	1: ___ SC Rate	
The scores are at the:	___Independent Level	___Instructional Level	___Frustrational Level	
Cues Used and Neglected			
On errors, the student predominantly uses:	___meaning cues	___structure cues	___visual cues	
On self-corrections, the student predominantly uses:	___meaning cues	___structure cues	___visual cues	
Processing Behaviors and Strategies			
At a point of difficulty, the student:	___self-corrects using different cues	___uses known words to solve unknown words	___waits to be told	
	___shows flexible use of strategies	___shows increasing control of visual patterns	___attempts unfamiliar words	
	___uses word meaning and context clues to problem-solve	___problem-solves at the point of error and makes multiple attempts to self-correct	___searches through the problem word and blends sounds together	
	___cross-checks cue sources	___searches for visual patterns	___reads high-frequency words fluently	
	___appeals for help	___rereads to confirm		
The student:	___reads word by word	___uses fluent phrasing	___uses expression	___uses punctuation
Comprehension/Retelling Check			
When retelling, the student's knowledge of the text's main idea:	___is lacking	___is teacher prompted	___is accurate	
When retelling, the student uses:	___no details	___few details	___several details	___extensive details

Oral Reading Record Analysis: Levels J/18–M/28

Directions: Use the prompts below to further analyze students' oral reading records.

Name _____ Date _____

School _____ Teacher _____

Text Title _____

Text Level _____ Seen _____ Unseen _____

Scoring			
Scores:	1: ___ Error Rate	___% Accuracy	1: ___ SC Rate
The scores are at the:	___Independent Level	___Instructional Level	___Frustrational Level
Cues Used and Neglected			
On errors, the student predominantly uses:	___meaning cues	___structure cues	___visual cues
On self-corrections, the student predominantly uses:	___meaning cues	___structure cues	___visual cues
Processing Behaviors and Strategies			
The student:	___uses nonfiction text features (table of contents, headings, glossary, index, diagrams, etc.) to locate information and read for a purpose	___decodes text using knowledge of sound/symbol relationships, including blends, digraphs, and irregular spelling patterns	___decodes text using context clues, word structures, inflectional endings, and simple prefixes and suffixes
	___integrates meaning, structure, and visual cues to decode and comprehend text	___reads fluently, only needing to problem-solve on one or two items	___problem-solves mostly "in the head" rather than in observable ways
	___applies flexible strategies with good control of visual patterns	___builds on background knowledge to make sense of text	___reads word by word
The student:	___uses fluent phrasing	___uses expression	___uses punctuation
Comprehension/Retelling Check			
When retelling, the student's knowledge of the text's main idea:	___is lacking	___is teacher prompted	___is accurate
When retelling, the student uses:	___no details	___few details	___several details

Oral Reading Record Analysis: Levels N/30+

Name_____   Date _____

School _____   Teacher_____

Text Title_____   Seen _____

Text Level _____   Unseen _____

Level I Analysis: Scoring

Error Rate _____   Easy_____

Accuracy % _____   Instructional_____

Self-Correction Rate_____   Hard _____

Level II Analysis: Cues Used or Neglected

Check the cue(s) that are predominantly used on errors:
☐ meaning   ☐ structure   ☐ visual

Check the cue(s) that are predominantly used in self-correction:
☐ meaning   ☐ structure   ☐ visual

Level III Analysis: Processing Behaviors and Strategies

Check the processing behaviors and strategies that are used:
- ☐ uses nonfiction text features (table of contents, headings, glossary, index, diagrams, etc.) to locate information and to read for a purpose
- ☐ decodes text using knowledge of sound/symbol relationships, including blends, digraphs, and irregular spelling patterns
- ☐ decodes text using context clues, word structures, inflectional endings, and simple prefixes and suffixes
- ☐ integrates meaning, structure, and visual cues to decode and comprehend text
- ☐ builds on background knowledge to make sense of text
- ☐ applies flexible strategies with good control of visual patterns
- ☐ reads fluently, problem solving on one or two things only
- ☐ most problem solving on text is done in the student's head and is not observable

Fluency   ☐ word by word   ☐ fluent phrasing   ☐ uses expression   ☐ uses punctuation

Level IV Analysis: Comprehension/Retelling Check

Knowledge of Main Idea			Use of Detail			
No	Teacher Prompted	Yes	None	Few	Several	Extensive

Assessing Reading Phrasing/Fluency, Intonation, Pace, and Accuracy

Name: _____ Date: _____

Reading phrasing/fluency, intonation, pace, and accuracy may be assessed any time a student reads aloud. Discuss the assessment rubric, modeling each description, so students know what you expect.

Rating Scale	PHRASING/FLUENCY
1	Reads word by word. Does not attend to author's syntax or sentence structures. Has limited sense of phrase boundaries.
2	Reads slowly and in a choppy manner, usually in two-word phrases. Some attention is given to author's syntax and sentence structures.
3	Reads in phrases of three to four words. Appropriate syntax is used.
4	Reads in longer, more meaningful phrases. Regularly uses pitch, stress, and author's syntax to reflect comprehension.
	INTONATION
1	Reads in a monotone and does not attend to punctuation.
2	Reads with some intonation and some attention to punctuation. Reads in a monotone at times.
3	Reads by adjusting intonation appropriately. Consistently attends to punctuation.
4	Reads with intonation that reflects feeling, anticipation, tension, and mood.
	PACE
1	Slow and laborious reading.
2	Reading is either moderately slow or inappropriately fast.
3	Unbalanced combination of slow and fast reading.
4	Reading is consistently natural, conversational, and appropriate, resembling natural oral language.
	ACCURACY
1	Exhibits multiple attempts at decoding words without success. Word reading accuracy is inadequate/poor, below 85%.
2	Attempts to self-correct errors are usually unsuccessful. Word reading accuracy is marginal, between 86–90%.
3	Attempts to self-correct errors are successful. Word reading accuracy is good, between 91–95%.
4	Most words are read correctly on initial attempt. Exhibits minimal self-corrections, all successful. Word reading accuracy is excellent—96% and above.

©2011 Benchmark Education Company, LLC

Reading Development Self-Assessment

"Metacognition refers to the student's conscious awareness of or knowledge about the reading and writing process, reading and writing strategies, and himself as a reader and writer. Metacognition is typically assessed through self-reports on questionnaires, interviews, or group discussions."

—Rhodes & Shanklin

The Reading Development Self-Assessment is a tool that can be completed individually by students and shared during individual reading conference discussions. Encouraging students to reflect on their understandings and growth as readers helps to identify individual goals and inform instruction.

Reading Development Self-Assessment

Name: _____ Date: _____

In the space below, record your thoughts about what you have learned about being a reader.

1. How do you select books to read independently?

2. Do you enjoy reading? Why, or why not?

3. What are some things you do well as a reader? How do these things help you as a reader?

4. What are some new things you've learned recently about being a reader? How have you changed as a reader?

5. What advice would you give a younger student about being a good reader? Why would this be good advice to follow?

6. What are you planning on reading next? Why?

7. What are some areas of need/things you would like to learn about being a reader?

Individual and Small-Group Reading Text-Level Progress Charts

Individual and Group Small-Group Reading Text-Level Progress Charts provide a profile of students' reading accuracy rates and text-level status.

Administration

1. After administering and analyzing Oral Reading Records, teachers can chart each student's progress on an Individual Small-Group Reading Text-Level Progress Chart. After individual charts are completed, a Group Small-Group Reading Text-Level Chart may be used to create a class profile.

2. For each group chart, record the date and the names of all students.

3. Record the students' performances on the texts they have read. Locate the title of the text read, and note the accuracy rate by recording a + for 90% or greater and a – for accuracy rates below 90%.

Using the Results

1. After completing the group chart, review your findings and determine potential members of future small-group reading groups, as well as proper text selection and level. Ask yourself the following questions regarding text difficulty: Was the text too difficult, too easy, or just right for the readers? Considering the problem-solving strategies used, was meaning maintained at all times?

2. Group Small-Group Reading Text-Level Progress Charts can be completed monthly in order to document the growth and progress of a class throughout the school year. Results can be shared with administrators and used to develop campus expectations and averages for learning over time.

3. Place the Individual and Group Small-Group Reading Text-Level Progress Charts in the appropriate organized storage location.

Individual Reading Text-Level Progress Chart

Name _____   **Date** _____

Chart Coding Symbols: **+** (90% or greater accuracy rate)   **–** (below 90% accuracy rate)

Title of text and reading level	Accuracy Rate	Comments:

Small-Group Reading Text-Level Progress Chart

Chart Coding Symbols: + (90% or greater accuracy rate)   – (below 90% accuracy rate)

Date _____

Grade _____

Student Names

Title of Text and Reading Level														

Year-at-aGlance Planning Calendar

Teacher Name: _____ Grade: _____ Level: _____

Notes:	August	September	October
	December	January	February
November		May	June
	March	April	

Informal Assessments for Reading Development

Month-at-a-Glance Planning Calendar

Teacher Name: _____ Grade: _____ Level: _____

	Monday	Tuesday	Wednesday	Thursday	Friday
Week of:					
Week of:					
Week of:					
Week of:					

Week-at-a-Glance Planning Calendar

Teacher Name: _____   Grade: _____   Level: _____

Progress-Monitoring Assessments					
Individual Reading Conferences					

Informal Assessments for Reading Development

Anecdotal Notes

Teacher Name: _____

Grade: _____ Level: _____

Adams, M.J., Foorman, B., Lundberg, I., and Beeler, T. *Phonemic Awareness in Young Children*. Brookes Publishing Company, 1998.

Afflerback, P. *Understanding and Using Reading Assessment, K–12*. IRA, 2007.

Anderson, C. *How's It Going? A Practical Guide to Conferring With Students*. Heinemann, 2000.

Barrentine, S., ed. *Reading Assessment: Principles and Practices for Elementary Teachers*. International Reading Association, 1999.

Bear, D.B., Invernizzi, M., Templeton, S., and Johnson, F. *Words Their Way: A Developmental Approach to Phonics, Spelling, and Vocabulary K–8*. Macmillan/Merrill, 1996.

Beaver, J. *Developmental Reading Assessment*. Celebration Press, 1997.

Beaver, T. *The Author's Profile: Assessing Writing in Context*. Stenhouse, 1998.

Boyd-Barstone, P. "Focused Anecdotal Records Assessment: A Tool for Standards-based, Authentic Assessment." *The Reading Teacher* 58 (3): 230–239. IRA, 2004.

Clay, M. *An Observation Survey of Early Literacy Achievement*. Heinemann, 1993.

Cobb, C. "Effective Instruction Begins with Purposeful Assessments." *Reading Assessment: Principles and Practices for Elementary Teachers* 2nd ed. 20–22. IRA, 2005.

Cunningham, P. *Phonics They Use: Words for Reading and Writing*. 3rd ed. Addison Wesley Longman, 2000.

Dorn, L., French, C., and Jones, T. *Apprenticeship in Literacy: Transitions Across Reading and Writing*. Stenhouse, 1998.

Dougherty Stahl, K. A. and Bravo, M. A. "Contemporary Classroom Vocabulary Assessment for Content Areas." *The Reading Teacher* 63 (7): 566–578. IRA, 2010.

Duke, N. and Pearson, P. D. "Effective Practices for Developing Reading Comprehension." In A. E. Farstrup, and S. Samuels (eds.). *What Research Has to Say About Reading Instruction* 204–242. IRA, 2002.

Fiderer, A. *Practical Assessments for Literature-Based Reading Classrooms*. Scholastic, 1995.

Fiene, J. M. and McMahon, S. "Assessing Comprehension: A Classroom-Based Process." *The Reading Teacher* 60 (5): 406–417. IRA, 2007.

Fletcher, R. and Portalupi, J. *Craft Lessons: Teaching Writing K–8*. Stenhouse, 1998.

Fletcher, R. and Portalupi, J. *Nonfiction Craft Lessons: Teaching Information Writing K–8*. Stenhouse, 2001.

Fountas, I. and Pinnell, G. *Guided Reading: Good First Teaching for All Children*. Heinemann, 1996.

Fountas, I. and Pinnell, G. *Matching Texts to Readers*. Heinemann, 1999.

Fountas, I. and Pinnell, G., eds. *Voices on Word Matters: Learning About Phonics and Spelling in the Literacy Classroom*. Heinemann, 1999.

Fry, E., Kress, J., and Fountoukidis, D.L. *The Reading Teacher's Book of Lists*. 3rd ed. Prentice Hall, 1993.

Gentry, J.R. *The Literacy Map: Guiding Children to Where They Need to Be K–3*. Mondo, 2000.

Gentry, J.R. *My Kid Can't Spell: Understanding and Assisting Your Child's Literacy Development*. Heinemann, 1997.

Gentry, J,R. and Gillet, J. *Teaching Kids to Spell*. Heinemann, 1993.

Gill, S. R. "The Comprehension Matrix: A Tool for Designing Comprehension Instruction." *The Reading Teacher* 62 (2): 106–113. IRA, 2008.

Glazer, S. M. *Assessment Is Instruction: Reading, Writing, Spelling, and Phonics for All Learners*. Christopher-Gordon, 1998.

Harvey, S. *Nonfiction Matters: Reading, Writing, and Research in Grades 3–8*. Stenhouse, 1998.

Harvey, S. and Goudvis, A. *Strategies That Work: Teaching Comprehension to Enhance Understanding*. Stenhouse, 2000.

Helman, L. A. "Using Literacy Assessment Results to Improve Teaching for English-Language Learners." *The Reading Teacher* 58 (7): 668–677. IRA, 2005.

Hill, B., Ruptic, C., and Norwick, L. *Classroom Based Assessment*. Christopher-Gordon, 1998.

Hindley, J. *In the Company of Children*. Stenhouse, 1996.

International Reading Association and National Council of Teachers of English. *Standards for the Assessment of Reading and Writing*. (revised) IRA, 2010.

Israel, S. E. *Using Metacognitive Assessments to Create Individualized Reading Instruction*. IRA, 2007.

Johnston, P. *Assessment Conversations. Reading Assessment: Principles and Practices for Elementary Teachers*. 2nd ed. IRA, 2005.

Johnston, P. *Knowing Literacy: Constructive Literacy Assessment*. Stenhouse, 1997.

Johnston, P. and Costell, P. "Principles for Literacy Assessment." *Reading Research Quarterly* 40 (2): 256–267. IRA, 2005.

Keene, E. and Zimmerman, S. *Mosaic of Thought*. Heinemann, 1997.

Lenski, S. D., Ehlers-Zavala, F., Daniel, M. C., & Sun-Irminger, X. "Assessing English-Language Learners in Mainstream Classrooms." *The Reading Teacher* 60 (1): 24–34. IRA, 2006.

McKenna, M. C. and Walpole, S. "How Well Does Assessment Inform Our Reading Instruction?" *The Reading Teacher* 59 (1): 84–86. IRA, 2005.

National Center on Education and the Economy. *Reading and Writing Grade by Grade: Primary Literacy Standards*. Smith Lithograph Corporation, 1999.

Opitz, M. and Ford, M. "Assessment Can Be Friendly!" *The Reading Teacher* 59 (8): 814–816. IRA, 2006.

Paris, A. H. and Paris, S. G. (2003). "Assessing Narrative Comprehension in Young Children." *Reading Research Quarterly* 38 (1): 36–76. IRA, 2003.

Pearson, P. D., Hiebert, E. H., and Kamil, M. L. "Vocabulary Assessment: What We Know and What We Need to Know." *Reading Research Quarterly* 42 (2): 282–296.

Pinnell, G. and Fountas, I. *Word Matters: Teaching Phonics and Spelling in the Reading-Writing Classroom*. Heinemann, 1998.

Power, B. *Taking Note: Improving Your Observational Notetaking*. Stenhouse, 1996.

Rhodes, L. and Shanklin, N. *Windows Into Literacy: Assessing Learners K–8*. Heinemann, 1993.

Risko, V. J. and Walker-Dolhouse, D. "Making the Most of Assessments to Inform Instruction." *The Reading Teacher*. February 2010.

Robb, L. *Easy to Manage Reading and Writing Conferences*. Scholastic, 1998.

Routman, R. *Conversations*. Heinemann, 2000.

Serafini, F. *Classroom Reading Assessment: More Efficient Ways to View and Evaluate Your Readers*. Heinemann, 2010.

Weaver, C. Reading *Process and Practice*. 3rd ed. Heinemann, 2009.